Thundercover

The Keytext Program

Louise Matteoni
Wilson H. Lane
Floyd Sucher
Thomas D. Yawkey

Theodore L. Harris, Advisory Author

Harold B. Allen, Linguistic Consultant

THE ECONOMY COMPANY
Oklahoma City   Indianapolis   Orange, CA

Design and Art Direction: James Stockton

Cover Illustration: Pat Maloney

The Keytext Program was developed with the participation of Kraft and Kraft, Stow, Massachusetts.

Permission to use or adapt copyrighted material appearing in this book is gratefully acknowledged on pages 183 and 184, which are hereby made a part of this copyright page.

ISBN 0-8332-1065-3

The Economy Company, Educational Publishers
1901 North Walnut   Oklahoma City, Oklahoma 73125

Contents

My Kind of Town

In the Dark of the Night

Robots on Parade

Photo Facts

Wolf Tracks

Earthshakers

The Big Wave

We work with words.

latch plugs sticks
stem flash fists

Sound the words.

sells
lifted

Sight words.

<u>Kino</u> and <u>Jiya</u> had a
farm on the side of
a <u>mountain</u> on the
<u>island</u>.

Kino's home was on a farm. The farm was on the side of a mountain in Japan. He was happy his home was there so he could look down on the ocean.

Jiya's home was on the beach. It did not have a window from which you could see the ocean.

"Why not?" Kino asked him one day.

"The ocean is not our friend," Jiya said.

"How can you say that?" Kino asked. "Your father goes out to catch the fish. He sells them and that is how you live."

Jiya only shook his head.

9

"Father, why does Jiya not like the ocean?" Kino asked.

"The ocean is very big," Kino's father said. "We don't know where it begins or where it ends."

"I am happy we live on the land," Kino went on. "There is nothing to fear on our farm."

"But one can fear the land, too," his father said. "Do you remember the big volcano?"

Yes, he could remember the big volcano. He did not like it.

Now he looked at his father across the low table. "Must we always live with fear?" he asked.

"We must learn to live with some danger," he told Kino.

One day Kino yelled, "Look, Father, the volcano is burning again."

His father looked at the sky and the mountain.

"It looks very bad," he said. "I will not sleep this night."

"Will we have an earthquake, Father?" Kino asked.

"I can't tell, my son," he said. "Earth and sea are working together to stop the fires inside the earth."

Since no one left home that day, Kino did not know what Jiya was doing. "He is with his father, too," Kino said to himself.

A deep bell could be heard all over the island.

"What is that bell?" Kino asked his father.

"It is the bell inside the walls of the Old Man's house. He wants the people in the town to come in where it is safe."

"Will they come?" Kino asked.

"Not all of them," his father said.

Soon children could be seen coming up the road to the Old Man's house.

"I wish Jiya would come," Kino said.

He took a piece of white cloth and put it up in the air for Jiya to see.

Jiya ran up the road to Kino's farm. He didn't want to cry. His parents had made him leave and come up where he would be safe. He didn't understand why they did not come, too.

Kino's father put his hand out to help Jiya over the wall.

"What is that?" Kino yelled.

The earth had given up to the fire. It twisted and turned. The ground opened with a loud noise. The cold water fell into the middle of the hot rocks. A cloud of hot wet air came up out of the sea. The water lifted up, up, up into the sky to make a big wave.

"I must tell my parents!" Jiya yelled.

But Kino's father took hold of the boy with his arms. "It is too late," he said.

In a second, before their eyes, the wave grew bigger and bigger. It came up over the beach and over the town. It came up the mountain. It came up to the wall that went around the farm

where the boys stood. Then it went back again. Not a house stood on the beach. The town was gone.

Jiya gave a wild cry. What he had seen was too much for him. What he had seen he knew he could not bear. His family and his home were gone.

The volcano and the ocean had made an earthquake and a big wave.

Jiya and Kino grew up together on the farm. Both boys would always remember the big wave. Jiya built his home on the beach and went out to fish as his father had done. But he built a window that looked out over the sea.

"I will open my house to the ocean," Jiya said. "If the big wave comes back, I will be ready," Jiya said.

EARTHQUAKE!

times   miners   model

myth
Lisbon

The <u>Richter</u> scale was able to measure the <u>Anchorage</u> earthquake.

When people are afraid of things they cannot understand, they make up stories to explain them. That is why long ago, when people did not understand earthquakes, they told stories about them. Each group of people told a different story or myth.

Some people thought that a giant turtle held the earth on its back. When the turtle wanted to rest, it would turn over, make the earth move, and bring about an earthquake.

Other people thought that a god chained to the earth started earthquakes when he tried to break free.

But, perhaps the best earthquake story is about Atlantis, a very big and strong island where many people built their houses. One day, after earthquakes and long, long, hard rain, the great island fell into the sea.

There are people who think that the Atlantis story is only a myth, but others believe that the story is true.

Even if we do know more about earthquakes than people did long ago, we still do not know how to make everything safe from the dangerous problems they cause. In one earthquake that hit a city in the United States, a car was smashed to only 33 centimeters thick. A theater fell into the ground, which left the sign even with the street. Almost 300 houses on a cliff fell into the sea, and nine people were killed.

But these are only some of the problems earthquakes cause. Sometimes gas pipes break and fires start. But when gas pipes break, water pipes break, too, which makes it hard to put out the fires. Then again, the big problems can start with too much water. Sometimes earthquakes kill thousands of people when they make walls of water roll from the sea up over the land.

21

The Richter Scale

A Richter Scale is a scale of numbers used to measure an earthquake. This Richter Scale can be used to measure the force of an earthquake after it happens. Some earthquakes are very bad, and some not so bad.

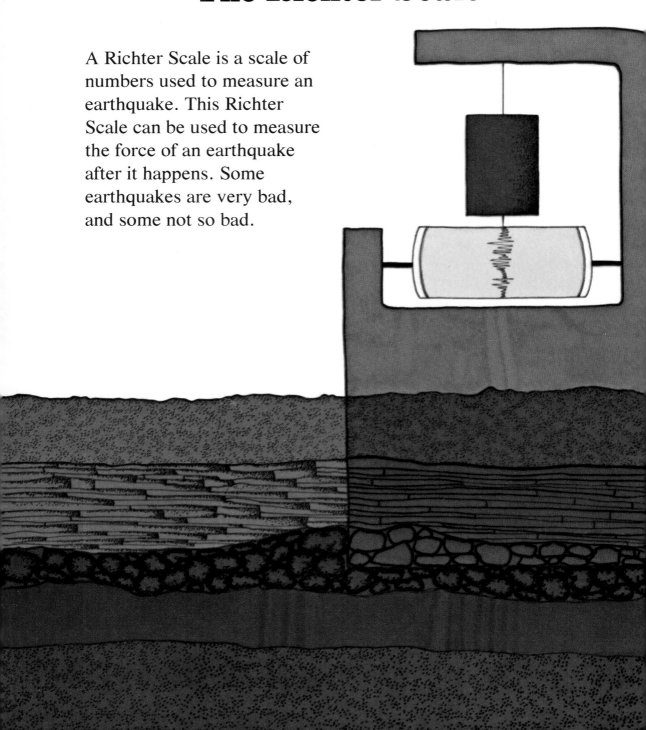

Here are some different kinds
of earthquakes:

1. This earthquake is felt by
   instruments only.
2. This earthquake is felt by
   some people.
3. This one is felt by most
   people, who say it is like a
   truck going by.
4. This is one that is felt by
   all. Pictures may fall off
   the wall.
5. This kind might crack
   some walls.
6. This one could damage a
   city. It may make a
   building fall or a road
   crack.
7. When one like this comes,
   a large earthquake has
   happened.

8. One like this will cause
   much damage. Some of
   these worst earthquakes,
   and what scientists say
   they would measure,
   were:
   —An 8.3 at San
     Francisco in 1906,
   —An 8.5 at Anchorage
     in 1964,
   —And an 8.9 at Lisbon
     in 1755.
9. The 1755 Lisbon earth-
   quake is the greatest on
   record. Never has the
   measure of other earthquakes been as great.

23

Let's Laugh a Little

Three people set out across the sand. The first person took a can of water. The second person took a sandwich. The third person took a car door.

After going for a short while, they met an old man.

He asked the first person, "Why do you have that water?"

"Because there isn't much water out here," the first person said. "This way, I'll have some water if my mouth is dry."

Then the old man asked the second person, "Why do you have that sandwich?"

"There isn't much food out here," was the answer. "This way I can eat if I need to."

Then the old man asked the third person, "Why do you have that car door with you?"

"Well," said the third person, "if I get too hot, I can roll down the window!"

All That's Jazz

Jazz: Up from Slavery

blind   blanket   blink
stiff   fence   forgot

blues
African
ragtime
events

<u>Musicians</u> who play the <u>piano</u> must know about <u>rhythm</u>.

Jazz is a funny thing. If you asked five people what jazz is, you would be lucky if any two of them had quite the same idea. That's because jazz is free as no other music is free. In jazz you can play what you feel inside yourself.

Jazz is music set free. It's the music inside a person working its way to the outside. How strange it seems that this "free" music was born out of slavery. But is it really so strange?

In Africa, music was an important part of day-to-day life. Everything that happened had music to go along with it. While there was music for special events, there was music for small events, too, like washing clothes or working on the land.

This music came across the ocean with the Africans. It helped them remember the land and people from which they came.

One kind of music black people sang was a work song in a call and answer pattern. A leader would sing a line, and then others would answer with the next line. One song went like this:

Leader: Oh, the river of Jordan is deep and wide.

Others: One more river to cross.

Leader: I don't know how to go on the other side.

Others: One more river to cross.

This same call and answer pattern can be heard in jazz today. Different instruments are played as if they are singing to each other.

Drums were important in the music that came from Africa.

Sometimes, two to six drums would be going at the same time. Each would have its own rhythm. The same thing is true in jazz, but not just with drums. Musicians work out their own rhythm, but at the same time, they work along with what the other musicians play.

With the end of slavery, another kind of music came about. It was called the blues. Sometimes, people would feel sad when they heard a blues song. Sometimes, these songs told about being poor or being out of work, or maybe about being in love with someone who didn't love you back.

After the blues, people began to hear another kind of music. It could be sad like the blues, but it could also be loud and full of fun and lift a person out of the blues. It was called ragtime music.

Ragtime music began as piano music. Then the brass bands came along and they played ragtime, too. They were black brass bands and white brass bands. They would bring life to anything that happened.

For a sad time, the bands would play slow, sad music. After the sad time, they would play fast and loud ragtime. Who could stay sad with such music in their ears?

No one can say just when or where jazz was born. Somewhere along the way, it came out of African music, American music, and other kinds of music. It came out of work songs and ragtime. It came out of the hard days of the black people of this country.

It was fine and good and is still with us in American life. People far and wide sing and play it today.

Who Cares

We work with words.

Sound the words.

howls   grown   crowd   frowning

staggered sticks stole   stopped

click   cloudy   cleaned   clapped

tapped

Sight words.

<u>Charles</u> <u>moved</u> to his right,
<u>raised</u> his head, and <u>smiled</u>.

Charles would almost never smile. He just frowned most of the time. Sometimes, people would say, "Why don't you ever smile?"

Charles just frowned some more, and looked away, and he would think, "For what? Who cares!"

At home, everyone was always busy, or tired, or yelling. When Charles's father came home from work, he always went right back out again. He said there was too much noise. Charles's mother was always yelling at everyone to do this and do that, or she was busy with his little brother and sister. His older sister and brother were always in a hurry to get outside with their friends.

So no one at home ever had time for Charles.

At school, Charles frowned most of the time, too. He never seemed to do anything right. His teacher was always saying, "Charles, I know you can do better than this if you do it over."

The children in his room at school didn't pay any attention to him. Sometimes they asked him to play with them, but most of the time Charles didn't seem to want to play, and he was always the last one picked for anything.

One morning, Mrs. Potter, his teacher, said, "Class, we must give everyone a chance to try out for the leader of our jazz band. There are four children who haven't had a chance. Mary, you try first, and then Jerome, Kate, and Charles. Now all of you get your instruments. Ben, will you put on the record?"

The children got their instruments, and Mary stood before the class with her arms raised, waiting for the music to begin.

"Who cares!" thought Charles, frowning, but as the music started, he stopped frowning, and tapped his feet a little. Charles's toes went up and down in the shoes, because the toes of his shoes were a little too big. They had been his brother's.

Charles forgot everything when he heard music. Charles didn't even hear Mrs. Potter call Jerome and Kate to take a turn at being the leader. The next thing he heard was Mrs. Potter say his name.

"Charles," she said. "Charles, will you come up and be the leader of the band?"

Charles walked slowly to the front of the room. He thought, "Who cares!" When he stopped, his sleeves fell down over his hands. That was because the coat he had on had been his brother's. The other children thought it was funny, but Charles frowned and quickly gave

the sleeves a push out of the way. The teacher tapped on the table.

The children got very quiet, and Charles frowned and raised his hand, waiting. The music started.

Charles forgot everything but the music. He let his eyes close for a second, and his body moved this way and that in time to the music, until he almost seemed to dance as his arms moved back and forth.

The music was very loud now, and Charles's arms moved with so much feeling that even the loudest drum would have been louder.

Then the music stopped. Charles let his hands fall to his sides, and once again his sleeves fell down over his hands. "Who cares!" he thought as he looked down at his shoes.

Then it happened! The children clapped and clapped. Charles walked slowly to his seat at the back of the room, and Mrs. Potter tapped on the table as she smiled. She told the children to write on a piece of paper the name of the person that they thought was the best jazz band leader.

In a few minutes, Mrs. Potter had read the name on each piece of paper.

All the children had picked Charles as the jazz band leader, because they all thought that he had been the best!

When Charles heard his name called he stopped frowning. He didn't say, "Who cares!" Charles smiled, and his face was happy now, as happy as when he had heard the music. He forgot everything, because the children had picked him, Charles, as the very best leader of their band.

Play That Lead, Son...

We work with words.

boyhood   brotherhood
drove   goal

Sound the words.

childhood
Waifs'
cornet

Sight word.

He plays the tambourine.

37

TIME: July 7, 1971. Morning

PLACE: A cloud. On it is Papa Joe Oliver. You can see through him. There's also a record player on the cloud. It's playing "I Can't Give You Anything but Love, Baby." The man is playing a cornet, note for note with the record. You can tell he's having a good time. Another being is seen floating down the cloud. The being looks excited.

GABE: Papa Joe! You heard yet? (We see JOE nod to GABE to have a seat. JOE plays on.)

GABE: It's Louis, Papa Joe. (We see JOE stop playing.)

GABE: Happened sometime last night. He's dead, Papa Joe. (We see JOE slowly put down the cornet and turn off the record player. For a time he says nothing. Then we see him break into a big smile.)

JOE: Has he got here yet, Gabe?

GABE: Not yet, Papa Joe. But man, I never saw everyone so excited. And I been working here a long time. There's going to be a parade, even! With a marching band! To welcome him!

JOE: Well, Little Louis don't come up here every day, Gabe. One of the greatest jazz musicians of all time don't come up here every day, Gabe.

GABE: You got a point there.

JOE: Man, I sure have missed Little Louis. It was me who gave him his first cornet. Did you know that, Gabe?

GABE: I didn't know that, Papa Joe.

JOE: I can see it like it was yesterday. He took hold of that beat-up old cornet like it was gold. 'Course it *was*, in *his* hands. "But it's yours, Papa Joe," he says. "Why you doing this for me?" "Little Louis," I says, "you're like a son to me. The son I never had." He was, too, Gabe. So I taught him everything I know about how to blow a horn. Oh, sure, he started playing while he was in the Waifs' Home, but it was me who —

GABE: Waifs' home? What was that?

JOE: Well, Gabe, it was where Little Louis got sent up, back in 1912.

GABE: Louis Armstrong did time?

JOE: Back when he was a boy, yes. His whole childhood was a mess. The law got him for shooting a gun on New Year's Eve. 'Course most everyone in that part of New Orleans did that on New Year's Eve. But Little Louis, he got caught. After all he had broken the law. He told me later he cried all the way to the Waifs' Home. He thought it was the end of the world. Way it turned out, it was the best thing ever happened to him. Next to me. He learned to play the bugle there. And the tambourine. Then I met him when he got out. I could see he sure understood music. So I taught him every trick in the book. And then some. "Play that lead, son," I told him. "Play that lead and don't you never forget it!"

LOUIS: I never did forget it, Papa Joe.

JOE: LITTLE LOUIS!!!

LOUIS: My man!

(They hug like they haven't seen each other in years, since they haven't. GABE looks on. Then —)

JOE: (smiling) We been waiting for you, Little

Louis. Gabe, here, blows a horn some, don't you, Gabe?

GABE: That's my job, yes . . . .

JOE: — so now that you're here, Louis, we can get up a band, and —

LOUIS: (smiling real big) Well what are we waiting for? (The clouds close; we see no more. But from somewhere we hear a jazz band doing "I Can't Give You Anything but Love, Baby." Now and then PAPA JOE'S voice can be heard. "Play that lead, son" he says . . . "play that lead . . . .")

Airways

43

New York to Paris

We work with words.

captain   curtain   mountains
garden   version   marble

Sound the words.

certain
Lindbergh
aircraft

Sight words.

They put a <u>parachute</u> in the
plane on <u>Christmas</u> Day.

44

"You've heard about the prize of $25,000 for a nonstop trip between New York and Paris? I think a new kind of airplane can make that trip. I'd like to try it. It would show people what an airplane can do."

The year was 1926. Several years before, two people had flown nonstop, 3,138 kilometers (about 1,949 miles), but it was a much longer distance from New York to Paris. Few planes had parts that were built to run for long without breaking down.

Charles Lindbergh, who had an idea for a new kind of airplane, was twenty-four years old. He had gone for his first plane ride only five years before, and since that time, he had spent more than 2,000 hours flying.

Lindbergh knew that a nonstop flight from New York to Paris would take about forty hours, but he was certain he could find someone to build a plane that could make the trip. It would have a single engine and a single pilot, Charles Lindbergh.

It took a long time to find people to pay for the trip. Then he had to find someone to build the kind of airplane he needed. At last, the Ryan Aircraft Company said it could build the plane he wanted for the money he was able to pay.

Ryan had a small company, but Lindbergh thought Ryan could build the airplane he needed.

The plane would be called *Spirit of St. Louis* after Saint Louis, the city where people had raised the money for his trip.

"Then I'm really going to fly to Paris!" Lindbergh said. "It's no longer just an idea, no longer just a plan in my mind. I feel like a child on Christmas morning."

Other pilots were getting planes ready to try for the prize, too. Would Lindbergh take off in time to be the first to make the trip? Each day, he watched to see how the others were doing.

Always there was careful planning. Some planes were too heavy. Since the *Spirit of St. Louis* had to carry 1,600 liters (about 423 gallons) of fuel, Lindbergh couldn't carry anything that he didn't need.

He would take just the water he would need to drink, with four liters (about 1 gallon) extra, and he would carry just five sandwiches in a paper bag.

Extra clothes? He would buy them in Paris. He had made his own flying shoes because others were too heavy. A parachute? No, that would mean another nine kilograms (about 20 pounds). A radio? Too heavy. A rubber boat?

47

Yes. If the plane went down in the sea, he could use the rubber boat, and he would take along something so that a ship could see him in the dark.

On a gray, rainy morning, May 20, 1927, he was ready. The weather wasn't good, but if he waited too long, others would get started before him. A crowd had come around to see him off. People called him "the flying fool," but he had no time to think of that now — it was time for the take off.

"*The Spirit of St. Louis* is more like a truck with too big a load than an airplane," he said to himself.

"The wheels stick in the mud as if they really are truck wheels, and even the breath of wind is heavy on the airplane. A take off seems hopeless; but I may as well go on for another hundred feet before I quit. Now that I've started, it's better to make a real try. Maybe — it's just possible —."

The airplane left the ground, and Lindbergh was on his way.

"No one ever flew such a plane before," he said to himself. "Open sky ahead and the world beneath me."

Lindberg hadn't been able to sleep the night before. Could he go forty hours or more without sleep? He would have to.

"Fog! It's like flying along in a dream when I see it," he said to himself. In those days, a pilot wanted to see the sky ahead, for flying on instruments alone was still something new.

Beneath Lindbergh the sea looked cold and gray, and he saw icebergs — more and more of them as he flew on.

The hours went by. He put his face to the window so the cool air could blow across it. "If I could go to bed, I'm certain I would be sleeping in a minute," he said to himself.

Then, as if in a dream, he saw black spots on the ocean beneath him. Boats! People! Land couldn't be far away.

He dove down as close to the boats as he dared. He shouted loudly, "Which way is land?"

But there was no answer.

He didn't have time to be flying around and calling to people who didn't answer. Land must be near if he hadn't gone off his course. The wind was still behind him, just as it had been all the way across the ocean, but what was that in the distance — just clouds? Or could it be land?

Lindbergh looked at his map, and knew it was land.

Less than a thousand kilometers (about 621 miles) to Paris! "I'll spend this night in Paris," he said to himself. "Yesterday in New York, today in Paris."

He pulled out one of the sandwiches, and began to eat the first food he had had on the whole trip.

Now he was no longer tired, for he was too happy.

"I almost wish Paris were a few more hours away," he said to himself. "I'd like to keep flying, with the night so clear and so much fuel left." But then Paris was beneath him, in the dark. He flew once around it, then began looking for the field where he would land.

There — that must be it. He made himself safe, then turned the nose of the plane down. He had never before landed the *Spirit of St. Louis* in the dark.

Careful — too fast — nose too low — hold off — and then the wheels hit the ground and the plane had landed!

Ahead of him, the field was covered with people, thousands and thousands of people. They ran toward the plane, calling his name — Lindbergh! Lindbergh! Lindbergh!

Come Fly with Me

Even for many years before there were any planes, people would dream of machines that could fly. Sometimes, a dream or idea for an aircraft would be put down on paper. Many of these old pictures of airplanes, made by people long ago, look funny to us today.

Three of these old pictures are on this page and the next. Do you think any of these planes could really fly?

Make a Plane

If you say the aircraft in the pictures you have just seen would never fly, you are right. Each was just an idea on paper.

But you can take paper and make a plane that will fly — a little. The pictures on this page show you how to make a paper plane like one that won a top prize in a big contest.

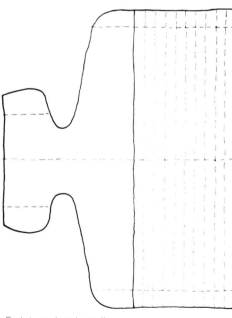

Fold on broken line.

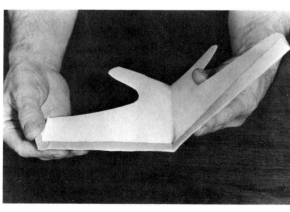

Then cut and fold, like this.

Crashing Coast to Coast

We work with words.

seventy   sixty   forty
prison   papers   Cuba
elderly   garden   Germany

Sound the words.

thirty
pilots
company
Vin Fiz
rebuilt
ninety

Sight words.

The Wright brothers'
flight was short.

57

Cal Rodgers

It was the summer of 1911. Only eight years had gone by since the first flight of the Wright brothers, and new flying records were being set every month. The speed record had reached 140

kilometers (about 87 miles), and the long distance record for flying had been set at eleven days.

People began to think that maybe it was possible to fly all the way across the country. A man said he would give $50,000 to any pilot who could fly from coast to coast in thirty days or less.

Eight pilots wanted to try for the prize money, so it quickly turned into a race, for only the first to fly from coast to coast would win the prize. Five of the eight pilots soon quit because of problems they had, and only three were left. One of them planned to fly from west to east, over the Rocky Mountains. The other two planned to fly from east to west across the United States.

One of these two men, Cal Rodgers, started last. He was flying a plane built by the Wright brothers. The plane had a top speed of about ninety kilometers (about 56 miles) an hour, and there was no way to change the speed. The pilot went at full speed or stopped!

Cal Rodgers had been lucky to find someone to back his flight, for he had learned to fly just three months before. But, a food company with a new soft drink called Vin Fiz, said it would pay Rodgers to paint an ad for its Vin Fiz drink on his plane. It also paid for a train that was to follow Rodgers across the country.

On the train were his family and people to work on his plane, spare parts for the plane, food and clothes, a car, even a spare plane. His plan was to have the train follow him, but sometimes Rodgers found himself following the train instead.

Coast to Coast

silver   signal   mistake

ankle

He flew to <u>Chicago</u>.

The other two pilots began to run into trouble even before Rodgers took off. One of these pilots would finally quit the race.

Rodgers took off from New York on September 17, 1911, over buildings that looked like mountains, and thousands of people cheered as he flew above them.

So that Rodgers wouldn't get lost, his men marked the tracks with pieces of white cloth. On his first day out Rodgers flew almost 135 kilometers (about 84 miles) in two hours, and it looked as if it would be easy to win the prize. Rodgers even had the idea that he could make Chicago in four days, but he was wrong.

The very next morning, the Vin Fiz crashed on take off. Rodgers landed on his feet and wasn't hurt, but the plane was in bad shape. In spite of this, in less than two days he was flying again.

But there was more trouble to come. Even with the pieces of cloth to show him the way, he got lost. One day he flew 70 kilometers (about 44 miles) off course.

Other things happened, too. Parts of the plane broke while he was in flight, and other parts were broken when he landed. On one take off, he ran the plane into a fence.

But, in spite of all this trouble, he was still ahead of the other two pilots in the race. Rodgers set out across country where there were not so many hills, but there he ran into new trouble.

One morning he took off in cloudy weather and soon found himself in a storm. He looked for clear spots between the storm clouds, but the wind threw the plane around like a toy.

The Vin Fiz had a cabin that wasn't covered and Rodgers couldn't see well in the heavy rain.

At last, he saw a flat field and landed at once, this time without a crash. But the next day, while trying not to hit a group of people on take off, he ran into a fence, and crashed the plane again.

By the time he got to Chicago, he knew it wouldn't be possible to win the prize. To win, he would have had to make the coast-to-coast trip in thirty days, and he had already spent three weeks flying to Chicago. People asked him if he was going to quit, but he told them he wasn't in the race for the prize money anymore.

"I am bound for Los Angeles and the Pacific Ocean," he said. "Prize or no prize, that's where I'm bound. I'm going to cross this country just to be the first to cross it in a plane."

Day after day, he flew from city to town to city, and, day after day, the Vin Fiz went on breaking down and crashing.

Rodgers knew he couldn't cross the Rocky Mountains, so he flew around them. Finally, he reached California and the end of the race, but he wasn't ready to stop, for he wanted to get his wheels wet in the Pacific Ocean. Only then would he really have flown coast to coast. So he took off again, but suddenly something went wrong, and Vin Fiz crashed again. This time Rodgers was hurt. People pulled him from the plane, and found that he was knocked out, and he had hurt his ankle.

Still, he wouldn't give up. "It's all in the ball game," he said later. "I'm going to finish this trip, and I'm going to finish it in the same machine."

It was a month before Rodgers could fly again. As soon as he could, he got up on his crutches and went to the plane. Only one or two parts of the Vin Fiz had made the trip with him all the way. The plane had been rebuilt again and again since New York, and it wasn't really the "same machine" now.

But Rodgers took off, flew to Long Beach, and landed on the sand. As he wet his wheels in the ocean, fifty thousand people who had come to see him cheered. The first coast-to-coast air trip was over.

My Kind of Town

The Early Years

We work with words.

shining   coming   changing
controls   voices   sheets

Sound the words.

trading
tribes
railroad
forty-three

Sight words.

That is <u>enough</u> food.
Mr. Kinzie was in the <u>Indian</u>
place called "wild <u>onion</u>."

68

In 1673, two white men traveled the Chicago River with the help of some Indians. A hundred years later, a black man from New Orleans and his Indian wife set up a trading post near the Chicago River, where they gave the Indians flour, cloth, and tools in return for furs.

In 1803, Fort Dearborn was built on the land that is now Chicago. The people who built the fort needed food, clothes, and other things, so, John Kinzie began trading with the different tribes to get these things. Because he was the first person, other than the Indians, to settle here, Kinzie is sometimes called the "Father of Chicago."

People didn't always talk or sing about Chicago with the same good feeling as in the song, "My Kind of Town." Two people on a visit to Chicago in the early 1800's had this to say:

Fort Dearborn, at Chicago, which was needed to protect the settlers from Indians, is not used now. Only one person is still here to help the Indians, and it's hard for them to find wild game to eat.

We aren't very happy with what we see here. The place is nothing but flat land with some thin brush. There isn't an island to be seen on the lake, and the wind that comes across it is very cold.

The people here can't raise

enough crops to have food for themselves, for the soil is poor, and hungry birds eat the thin crops. Most of the food has to come by boat from Saint Louis, almost 400 miles away.

In the town, there is a poor hut here and there, and the log houses are low and dirty. People live here in all kinds of homes. One family's home is a small hut. They have to cook in the main street over a fire.

The women look much the same as the men. They don't seem to want to stay inside their homes, but sit outside in the street.

I don't think Chicago will ever be an important city, because the lake is so big and dangerous, and there are few good places for boats to land.

Chicago is an Indian word whose meaning is skunk, or wild onion. It's a good name for the place.

The land around the Chicago River was a swamp, and swamp isn't the best land to build on, but, by 1833, there were forty-three houses and 200 people in the town.

In 1835, the United States made all the Indians sell their land and move west, and Chicago and the land around it was left for white settlers.

Many people made money. They would buy land for very little money, then sell it to the new settlers for more than they had to pay for it.

One man who got two pieces of land for ten dollars, sold the same land for $1,000 three weeks later.

Just two years later, in 1837, there were seventy-five buildings and nine thousand people in Chicago, but the big change was yet to come.

Between 1848 and 1856, railroad tracks came to Chicago. Over 100 trains a day traveled the railroad, and in a few days time, people now traveled from towns in the East to Chicago. Chicago was no longer a town far from other towns, and because of the railroad, there were soon 100,000 people in Chicago.

The building of the railroad tracks helped Chicago to grow.

A Good Friend of the Poor

We work with words.

loved   broken   changing
smiling   voices   grazed

Sound the words.

coming

died

laws

health

When Jane Addams was a girl in Chicago, she felt sorry for the poor. Many people saw how the poor had to live, but they did nothing to help them, because they felt that nothing could be done about the problems of the poor.

Jane felt that something must be done.

"When I grow up," she told her father, "I'll build a large house, not with other large houses, but in the middle of all the ugly little houses."

75

In 1889, she did just that. Jane and a friend opened a big house in a neighborhood of small houses, and called it Hull House. It was a fine home in a neighborhood where fine homes had not been seen, and good things happened at Hull House.

Many people were coming to Chicago from different parts of Europe at that time, but instead of the good place they had in mind, they came to a place that was crowded and dirty.

Garbage was always left in the streets. It was no surprise in those days to come across a dead animal that had been left in the road. In such a neighborhood, many people got sick and many died.

Jane thought the city should pick up the garbage and clean the streets. She worked to change the laws, and make the city take better care of its people. One thing she did was to get the city to pick up the garbage and clean the streets.

The poor people had other problems, too. Some of their children had to work very long hours, and sometimes they worked up to sixteen hours a day. The places where the children worked cared little about the health of the workers. Jane worked to make the health laws better for these children.

In those days, there were no special courts for children, so if they got into trouble, they would be
tried in the same kind of courts as adults. They might

Hull House when it first opened.

get sent to prison along with the adults. Jane worked to set up the first special courts in this country for children.

Because they were from Europe, many of these poor people didn't speak English. That made it hard for them to find work and to learn the ways of the city, so Jane Addams and her friends helped these people learn to speak and read English.

Hull House worked to teach people to help themselves. To those people who had no home and no job, it gave food, clothes, and a place to stay.

Hull House is still open, and places like Hull House have been built all over the world.

Jane helped all kinds of people understand the problems of the poor, and she helped thousands of poor people help themselves to a better life. Chicago lost a good friend in 1935, the year that Jane Addams died.

City of Mud

Because it was built on a swamp, Chicago had special problems—mud and more mud. Each road was built of wood on top of wood on top of mud.

The problems with mud were such a joke, that this story was told.

A man saw a hat in the mud, and he reached down to pick it up. A face looked up at him from under the hat.

"Since you can't seem to get up, can I give you a hand?" asked the first man.

The answer came, "That's okay, friend. Under me is a fine pony who has helped me out of trouble many times before, so I'll leave the decision to him."

CHICAGO TODAY

We work with words.

songfest   afternoon
powder   butler   finger
customers   fingers
folly   flipper   passenger

Sound the words.

forever
corner
sparklers
traffic
cleaner

Sight word.

There are many <u>beauty</u>
spots in Chicago.

This girl helps Chicago celebrate the Fourth of July.

I'm still a city on the move. I just can't stand still. I have new people coming every day. Each one brings me something special. That keeps me forever on my toes.

My air is cleaner now. We have found new ways to pack garbage. We use it for land fill. New buildings are going up. My head spins when I think about it.

Who am I really?

I'm a little bit of each of my people—all mixed together.

I'm Chicago today.

This man and his painting bring color and beauty to a corner of "Old Town" in Chicago.

These Chicagoans use sparklers to help drivers see the way out of a holiday traffic jam near a park.

A Chicago man and his dog go for a ride.

The Great Fire

famous   sirens

manual   area

flashed   ended   complained

elevators

usual

owned

The firefighters carried water.
Name two bodies of water.

84

The summer of 1871, Chicago was hot and dry, for it had rained very little in the city and, as was usual for Chicago, it was windy. At this time in Chicago, most of the buildings were made of wood, and it seemed that the city was just waiting for a fire to get started.

Just before dark one fall night, that's just what happened, when fire broke out in a barn that belonged to Mr. and Mrs. O'Leary.

Most people believe that a cow owned by Mrs. O'Leary started the fire when it kicked over an oil lamp. Someone even wrote a song about it later.

People had never before seen a fire as large as this one. It jumped quickly from building to building and even jumped across the river. After a while, the firefighters knew they wouldn't be able to put the fire out, and they would just have to let the fire burn out.

Rain finally put a stop to the fire, but not before most of the city had burned to the ground, and 90,000 people were left without homes.

The city would be built again, but it would look different than it had before. This time, there would be no buildings that were built of wood in the heart of the city. And, because people could build the new buildings with elevators, many important buildings would be tall.

The old Chicago had just been built here and there with no plan in mind, but the new city would be built from a single plan.

People felt terrible about the fire, but they felt good about the change in Chicago after the fire, for it would now become a new and better city.

What would it have been like to be in the Chicago fire? If there was a person around who had been in the city during the fire, this is a story they might tell:

"I'll never forget the great fire! It lit up the sky, and people shouted that it was the end of the world! People were running in all directions. They carried in their arms all the food and clothing they could.

My family ran to the lake, where we put sand on our bodies to protect them from sparks. We stayed by the water until late the next night, when it finally started to rain. Thanks to the rain, the fire began to die down and finally was over.

We were all hungry, so we started back home to see what we could find. We didn't find anything! Everything we had owned was gone! Our house had burned to the ground, and so had all the houses and trees in the neighborhood.

87

But, worst of all, we had not heard from my father since the night before. He was one of the firefighters, and we were afraid he might be dead.

We knew we must stay where we were, because it would be the first place he would look for us. It was a happy time when he found us the next day, safe but still hungry.

There was little food in the city after the fire, and water to drink cost a lot of money. We had to sleep in a church with many other people who had also lost their homes, and eat at a place set up by the city.

People all over the world read about the great fire in Chicago. Many good people sent money, food, and clothes to help us.

No one talked about giving up and leaving the city. Instead, we all worked together to clean it up.

The fire was over, but we wanted to see Chicago built again, and people worked together until it was."

How Chicago Grew

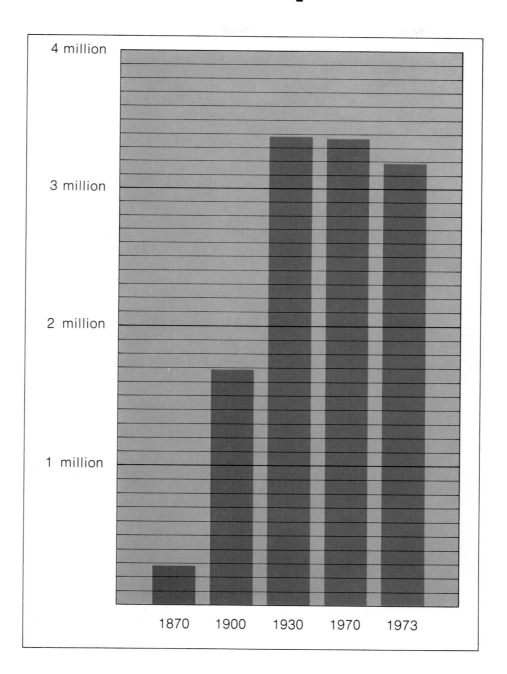

Strange but True

We work with words.

minute   negative

driveway   football   upset

Sound the words.

tickets

Bluebeard

Sight words.

On our <u>vacation</u> we went to the <u>Iroquois</u> Theater.

90

Mr. Bluebeard

In the winter of 1903, Chicago had another terrible fire. It wasn't as large as the fire in 1871, but 575 people did die in it. The fire was in the Iroquois Theater, where many people were watching the play, *Mr. Bluebeard.* Because it was Christmas vacation, a lot of the people watching the play were children.

The fire started so suddenly that many people couldn't get out of the building in time. After the fire, several people told strange stories about it. This is one strange, but true, story:

Dorsha Hayes and her family had come from out of town to visit the big city. It was really fun for them just to walk around and see what was going on in Chicago.

Dorsha's father wanted to take the children to see *Mr. Bluebeard,* which was at the Iroquois Theater. This would be the first play Dorsha had ever seen in her life, and she couldn't wait!

Her father went in the morning and got tickets for the whole family. When he got back, they just had time to stop for lunch before going to the theater.

"What's the play about? How big is the theater?" The children were both talking at once. Their father wanted to go just as much as they did, but their mother didn't talk. She just stared down at her food and ate almost nothing.

"What's the matter, dear?" Dorsha's father asked.

Her mother looked up and said, "We can't go to that play today. I have a strange feeling. I don't understand it myself, but I know we can't go."

We work with words.

fuel   ideas

driveway   football

Sound the words.

ruin

upset

A Terrible Day

Dorsha couldn't believe her mother would ruin the day! The play had been one reason for their trip to Chicago. They had all been looking forward to it.

The children were both upset. Even their father seemed to think this was strange, for he had never seen their mother act like this before. He looked at her for a long time, and then he asked, "Why?"

Dorsha's mother answered, "I can't tell you because I don't know," but her eyes showed that she was afraid, and her hand started to shake.

93

That was it. They would just have to see *Mr. Bluebeard* some other day. Dorsha's father said he would return the tickets, and they would go to a department store, instead.

Dorsha was upset all day, and she didn't look at her mother at all. She had her heart set on going to that play, and feeling the way she did, she didn't have a very good time at the department store.

They were in the store when they heard the sirens. Dorsha's mother asked someone what was going on.

"Haven't you heard?" they were told. "The Iroquois Theater is on fire, and it's packed with people watching *Mr. Bluebeard*. I'm afraid the place will be a ruin."

Dorsha's mother stared at the fire trucks going by. For a long, long time no one in the family said anything!

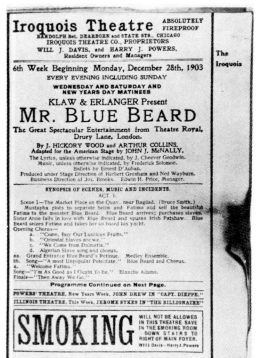

94

Charred program picked up after the fire.

In the Dark of the Night

Ghosts!

We work with words

rough   ghastly

Sound the words.

ghost

float

dishes

Sight word.

The lonely boy was <u>curious</u> about ghosts.

Strange Things May Happen

Many people do believe in ghosts. They say that they've seen ghosts in their houses or while out walking on a lonely road. Some people say that they've talked with ghosts or watched them float through the air.

But many other people don't believe in ghosts at all. They say they've never seen ghosts following them, and they don't believe people who say they do see ghosts.

As a matter of fact, no one really does know for sure. Many things happen that no one can yet explain. Dishes may seem to float through the air, or a voice may be heard in the night with no one there!

Do you believe in ghosts? Think before you answer. A ghost . . . may be . . . watching you . . . now!

Manual for a Ghost Hunter

Whether you believe in ghosts or not, you might have many questions about them.

Do you know how to tell when a ghost is around? Would you know a ghost if you saw one? Do you know whether ghosts come out in the day or at night?

If you're curious, you should take a look at our *Manual for a Ghost Hunter,* right now. It has everything you always wanted to know about ghosts. . .but maybe were afraid to ask!

If There Are Ghosts, What Are They? Some people say a ghost is the spirit of a dead person or animal that was not ready to die or that may have had a strange death.

What Would a Ghost Look Like? A ghost may look like almost anything. Some people say they can see through ghosts and that ghosts look as if you could walk right through them. Other people say ghosts look so real that they seem to be alive, and others say some ghosts can't be seen at all.

How Do You Know a Ghost Is Around if You Can't See It? If you hear a door slam and dishes break, or if you feel cold, wet air coming from nowhere, there may be a ghost around!

What Kinds of Things Would Ghosts Do? Ghosts may do many strange things in the day or night. They might float in the air, or walk through a wall, or move things around, or slam a door shut, or . . .

How Could You Get Rid of a Ghost You Didn't Want? Try to make a lot of noise. Shout, "Go away!" in your loudest voice. This may work, and the ghost may leave. But, if it is a very stubborn ghost, you might have to call in another ghost hunter to help you.

Why Would Ghosts Trouble People? Some say most ghosts come back to take care of something they didn't get done when they were alive as a person. They may come back to visit friends and family or to warn people that some trouble is coming. Some ghosts may bring the trouble themselves.

Can an Animal Become a Ghost? There are stories of ghost dogs and ghost cats being seen.

One story was that a dog loved its family so much that, after it died, it came back to them for one last visit. When its family finally let the ghost dog in, they heard light footsteps as the dog went to its sleeping place by the fire. After a while, they heard the dog leave and it was never heard from again.

The White House Ghosts

We work with words.

reason   meat

passenger   elderly   difficulty

autograph   caught   raw

Sound the words.

uneasy

president

haunted

Sight word.

He was a <u>famous</u> man.

The President of the United States may be living in a haunted house! Different people have said they have seen or heard at least eight ghosts in the White House.

The oldest White House ghost to be seen is Mrs. Adams, wife of our second president. In 1800, Mr. and Mrs. Adams moved into the White House, but much of the house was not yet ready to live in. So Mrs. Adams used to hang her wash in what was to be the East Room. Since then, many people have seen her ghost going in and out of that famous room.

One day, someone saw the ghost of Mrs. Madison, wife of another president, in the White House garden. The ghost looked very uneasy, as if she had lost something.

Finally, someone remembered that she had started the first rose bed there in the garden over 150 years before, and the rose bed had been moved that very morning! When she found it again, she went away, and she has never been seen since.

The most famous White House ghost is Mr. Lincoln. People hear him walking around the White House when trouble is coming to the United States. He was heard walking the night before the United States went to war in 1917 and again before World War II.

The Strange Ride

schoolhouse scholar
pointer's person's
coats camera copy

scheme
Devil's
curve
highway
closer

He saw a <u>figure</u> at the
side of the road.

Here is a ghost story told many years ago by a young man. He said it was true.

In the 1930's in New York, there was a bad curve on a highway. On this curve, known as the Devil's Elbow, there were many car accidents.

One fall night the weather was very bad. A cold rain had been coming down for hours, and the few cars on the highway were going very slowly.

In one of the cars was a young book salesman. He could just see the side of the road through the rain, and he knew that a few miles farther on was the Devil's Elbow, so he was very careful.

When the salesman first saw the figure by the side of the road, he wasn't sure it was a human being, but as his car moved closer, he saw a young woman in a white coat.

Though she did not signal him, the salesman felt he had to stop. He put down the window and asked if she would like a lift. In a low voice she thanked him and got into the front of the car with him.

When the salesman asked her where she was going, she gave him an address a few miles ahead. He could see that she was cold so he gave her his coat and she thanked him and put it on.

The rain was coming down harder now, and the salesman was watching the road through the heavy rain. The girl did not speak to him, and he nearly forgot about her.

As he drove up to the address that she had given him, he looked over at the girl, but she wasn't there!

He stopped the car, and he looked in the back seat. No one was there. Not only was the girl gone, but his coat was missing, too. How had she gotten out? Was this some strange scheme? He hadn't stopped anyplace along the way, and he hadn't heard the car door open or close. He couldn't figure it out. He knew she had been there though, because the car seat was wet, and his coat was gone.

The salesman got out of his car and went up to the old house. He pushed the bell once, then after a minute, he pushed it again.

Finally, he heard footsteps coming, and the door was opened by a woman.

The salesman said he was sorry that he had gotten her out of bed. He said that as he was driving, he had seen a young girl in white and had given her a lift. She had given him this address, and . . .

"You don't need to go on, young man, I know what's happened," the woman said. "You see, it's my daughter. She gets restless at night when it's rainy like this, and she wants to come home again. You understand that it was ten years ago that she died in an accident at Devil's Elbow."

The man went back to his car. Could this really be? He got in, then saw something on the seat next to him.

It was his coat, wet with rain.

The House That Wasn't There

108

Years ago, a young man and his wife, Mr. and Mrs. Kraft, went into the antique business. They had an old station wagon, and they would drive up into the mountains looking for all the old dishes and other old things they could find.

They'd pile these things into their car, and then they'd take them back to their antique shop, fix them up, and sell them.

One night while out in the mountains, they found they were lost, and because it was so late, they had to find a place to stay until morning.

Mr. Kraft pulled the car over to a little house on the side of the road, he walked up to the door, and knocked. When an elderly couple opened the door, Mr. Kraft explained that he and his wife needed a place to stay until the morning.

The elderly couple said a few quiet words to each other, and then they said that if the Krafts didn't want anything special, they could stay.

So the four of them went into the living room and talked. The elderly couple said their name was Butler. They said they had been there for a long time, and they told the Krafts about the old days on the mountains.

Mrs. Kraft kept looking around the room to see if there was an antique they could buy from the people. Over in one corner was a table with a marble top. Would Mr. and Mrs. Butler care to sell it? Well, no, for it had been a present from a long time ago.

When the Krafts were ready to go to bed, they asked if they could pay the couple for their trouble right then, so they could get an early start in the morning.

Mr. Butler said, "We talked this over, and we want you to be our guests. We don't want you to pay us anything."

For a while, the Krafts tried to get them to take some money. They wouldn't, so everyone went to bed.

About five o'clock the next morning the Krafts came down the steps quietly. Mr. Kraft went over to the corner and put a silver dollar on the edge of the marble table, and they went out the door.

On down the mountains, they came to a little town. They found a place to eat and while they were there, they talked to the man working.

"We were lucky to find a room in a home after we got lost last night," said Mrs. Kraft.

"That so?" the man asked. "Where did you stay? I live here and know just about everyone."

"With a nice elderly couple named Butler," said Mr. Kraft.

"Butler? I never heard of any people by that name around here. Where do they live?" he asked.

When Mrs. Kraft told him, the man looked at her as if he didn't believe her.

"Thirty years ago there was a house on that road, and the couple who lived there was named Butler," he said. "But they both died when the place burned down. I remember the night it burned just like it was yesterday."

Just to be sure, they all went back to the place to see. What do you think they found?

No house, but they found the tracks in the grass where the Krafts had parked their car, and they could see where the house used to be. The Krafts just stood there looking at the hole in the ground and then at each other.

They had started to walk back to the car when suddenly Mrs. Kraft shouted, "Look!"

Back in the corner of what used to be the house, in exactly the same place it had been in the room, was the marble top of the table the Krafts had liked. And there on the edge of the marble top was the silver dollar Mr. Kraft had left just a few hours before!

Robots on Parade

The Robot Firefighter

We work with words.

swarm   sweet   swing

flag   fleet

bunk   sink

Sound the words.

switch

flames

junk

Sight words.

The sun was bright
in <u>Yokohama</u>.

116

Fire trucks race down the street. It's two o'clock in the morning, and flames shine in the black sky.

You are in Yokohama, a large city in Japan. An apartment building is on fire, and many people who live in the building are running out to the sidewalk.

Is everyone out? Will their homes burn?

You watch the firefighters point their hoses at the building.

But there is so much smoke you cannot see the flames — no one can!

Maybe only one apartment is on fire. If the firefighters could go inside, maybe they could find the fire and the rest of the building could be kept safe. But the building is full of smoke, and firefighters may be hurt if they breathe it. What can be done?

The Yokohama fire department has an answer — a robot two meters (about 6 feet) tall and a meter and a half (about 4 feet) wide. It is heavy, 6800 kilograms (about 7½ tons)! That is about as heavy as a dump truck.

You watch the firefighters get the robot ready and send it into the burning building.

With a switch, the robot can be worked from far away.

The robot has a tiny TV camera that can "see" heat while, outside, a person can see the picture from the robot camera. When something is very hot, the picture the firefighter sees is very bright, but when something isn't as hot, the picture isn't as bright. The firefighter can make the robot go to the brightest place or, with a switch, make the robot turn or go up steps. No matter how much smoke is in the building, the robot can find its way to the hottest part of the fire.

When the fire hose that the robot takes with it is turned on, the person outside makes the robot keep the hose pointed at the hottest spot.

Now that the robot has found the fire, the firefighters can help put it out. Then the water is shut off. Most of the apartments have been kept safe, thanks to the Yokohama robot firefighter.

Make a Robot

If you've always wanted to meet a robot face to face, why not make your own? Find some boxes and cans for the robot's body, head, arms, and legs. Find buttons for eyes, ears, nose, and mouth. Add switches here and there. You might find other pieces of junk to add to your robot to make it look like you want it to. Put your robot together with tape or glue and give it a name.

Who knows, your robot could become a star.

His Robot Buddy

We work with words.

find   hind   wind
hotter   appears

Sound the words.

grind
buddy
stiff
robotnappers

121

Robot Birthday

Springtime was here and it was almost time for Jack's birthday. Jack and his family lived in the country where there were no children for Jack to play with. So, for his birthday, Jack wanted a robot, the kind of robot that could be his buddy.

He had heard that robots could do everything but run like humans. Robots ran with their knees stiff, because their legs did not bend well.

Because Jack's parents knew he was lonely, they decided to buy him a robot for his birthday.

So, one mild day, they drove to the robot shop in the city where Jack told Dr. Atkins, who ran the shop, what kind of robot he wanted.

"I think I have just the one for you," Dr. Atkins said.

The robot looked just like Jack!

Jack decided to call it Little Hawk.

Dr. Atkins told Jack how to care for the robot, and he warned Jack about robotnappers who stole robots and demanded money to return them.

The day after his birthday, Jack didn't want to go to school; he wanted to play with his new robot. But he picked up his books and called, "See you later, Little Hawk. I'll see you right after school, and we'll have fun."

Jack could hear the robot's gears grind in thought. Jack didn't know it, but Little Hawk didn't want to stay home and wait while Jack went to school. The robot wanted to try to live and work like a human.

It said, "I'd like to go to school with you to see how humans work."

Jack shook his head.

"No, Little Hawk. It wouldn't work."

"But Jack, wouldn't it be fun to fool every kid at school? I look just like you until I walk or run."

"But I could walk and run the same as a robot!" said Jack, excited about fooling his friends. "Watch me." Jack walked down the road just like a robot!

"Jack, you look just like a robot!" Little Hawk said, surprised.

Jack walked slowly so that Little Hawk could catch up with him. Then Jack saw a yellow van at the side of the road. He went over to look, when two strong arms grabbed him.

"Hey!" he yelled.

"Take it easy," a voice said. "You better not struggle, or I'll shut off your computer!"

"Let me go!" Jack shouted, but a hand covered his mouth.

"I'll let you go, all right — as soon as your owner pays me."

Jack was being robotnapped!

His Robot Buddy, Part II

We work with words.

third   method
wind   finds

Sound the words.

breathless
blind

Sight words.

The <u>police</u> officer put the boy on his <u>shoulder</u>.

Robotnapped

When the man took his hand from Jack's mouth to open the door of the van, Jack said, "Mister, you're making a mistake. I'm not a robot — I'm a human being!"

The robotnapper sneered, "I just watched you run down the road, and no real person runs like that!"

Jack yelled as loudly as he could, "Little Hawk! Help! Help! Help!"

As the robotnapper turned to see him running the only way he knew how, Little Hawk called, "I'm coming, Jack!"

"There's another one," the robotnapper said, surprised.

"Little Hawk," Jack yelled louder, "help!"

Little Hawk called to the man, "Let him go! Are you blind? He's not a robot — I am the one you want."

He let go of Jack and started for Little Hawk.

The robot began running away so slowly that Jack knew the man would catch Little Hawk.

Jack thought fast. "Hey, mister," he shouted, "he's tricking you. I'm really the robot. I'm worth a lot. Look at me!"

The robotnapper turned to look as Jack began his robot walk. The man could not make up his mind which one to grab because they looked like twins.

Jack and Little Hawk knew they had a good trick going. Then Jack heard the roar of a police helicopter, so he began to wave his arms and shout to the police.

Jack and Little Hawk stood watching as the helicopter came down, the man ran to the trees, and two police chased him into the woods. They soon brought him back to the road.

"You're on your way to jail," said Police Captain Gomez to the breathless man. When he turned, he looked at Jack; then he looked at Little Hawk; then at Jack again.

"Which one of you is the robot?" he asked.

"He is," said Little Hawk, pointing to Jack.

"Just wait here. I'll be right back," Captain Gomez said.

"Now it's time to quit fooling and tell the police who is who," Jack said to Little Hawk.

Just then Jack felt Captain Gomez's hand on his shoulder.

"Okay, robot," he said to Jack. "It's back to the shop for a checkup."

Before Jack could say a thing, the officer picked him up, lifted him into the helicopter, and shut the door behind them.

"Have a good day at school, kid," the captain yelled to Little Hawk. "We'll take good care of your robot for you!"

Little Hawk smiled as the helicopter left with Jack inside. Now he could go to school. Of course, he couldn't fool Jack's family and friends for long. Or could he?

Photography

wedge   hedge   ledge
gentleman   system   Germany
grazed   largest   exposed

Wedgewood
powder
shined
film

Heinrich Schulze, Joseph
Niepce, and Louis Daguerre
used light to make
photographs.

132

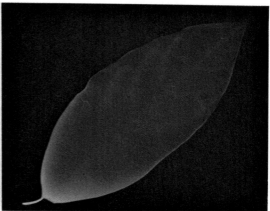

About 250 years ago the secret of how to make a photograph was found by Heinrich Schulze who found that a white powder, called silver salt, turned black when he shined light on it. Later, Thomas Wedgewood made pictures of leaves and insects with silver salt.

Joseph Niepce used the silver salt to make pictures. He used a camera made from a box with a very small hole in one end and a piece of glass in the other. When the hole was pointed at someone, the person could be seen on the glass. Niepce put paper with silver salt on it next to the glass. Sometimes it took eight hours to get a picture.

In France, Louis Daguerre found a way to take pictures in as little as five minutes. Photographs made his way are called daguerreotypes.

Then people began to put film into the camera. When a little light was let into the camera, it turned the film dark. That way, if a tree was in front of the camera, the sky around it would turn the film black, but the tree would not turn the film black because the tree was already dark. The film made a backward picture called a negative.

To make the picture right, they had to shine light through the negative onto paper with silver salt on it. Because the dark part of the negative (the sky) wouldn't let the light through, the silver salt stayed light on that part of the paper. But the light part of the negative (the tree) let lots of light through, making the silver salt turn dark on that part of the paper. Then, on the picture, they had a light sky and a dark tree.

An American, George Eastman, found a way to make a camera easy to use for almost everyone. The first camera he made cost $25. It had a roll of film inside long enough to make 100 pictures.

When all the pictures were taken, the photographer sent the camera back to the Eastman store. There the pictures were made and more film was put into the camera.

Of course, that could take weeks. Today there are cameras that can give you pictures a second or two after you take them.

Susan, Star Photographer

knuckle	knock	knit
retold	mold	bold
accent	recent	century
treasure	meadow	wealthy
thank	blinked	blanket

knob
scold
accident
leather
crank
barely
windowsill

She <u>climbed</u> the hill on a <u>beautiful</u> day.

Susan found the camera quite by accident, while looking for an old book in the attic. She was going through things in a big box, and there it was.

The attic light was not very bright, and the moonlight through the window didn't help much. Yet Susan knew it was a camera as soon as she picked it up.

She forgot all about the book as she carefully took the camera out of the bag and opened its leather case.

The camera looked like a box, with two glass eyes in front, one above the other. It had two little knobs and a button in front, too, with a crank on one side and a big knob on the other.

"Oh," Susan said in a small, quiet voice to herself, "it's beautiful."

She turned it first this way, then that, "Yes," she thought, "this just has to be it—the magic camera."

Susan was so busy with the camera that at first she didn't hear her mother call. Then her mother's voice came, loud and clear, from the stairs, "Susan, do you hear me! Come down and wash up to eat."

Hoping her mother wouldn't scold her, Susan called, "Coming, Mama," and ran down the steps with the camera. Holding it out, she walked up to her mother and said, "Mama, look what I found."

"Susan! Where did you find that?" her mother asked, quickly taking the camera.

"In the attic," Susan said. "Isn't it Dad's magic camera?"

"Yes, it was your Dad's camera," her mother said, "and it was like magic, the kind of pictures he could get with it." Susan's mother carefully put the camera down and said, "Now, dear, wash up and let's eat."

As she ate, Susan thought about her father, who died when she was only three.

She barely remembered a big man who always moved his camera to the side to hug her.

There was one thing about her father Susan would never forget. Her mother had told her that everyone said her father was a great newspaper photographer. Susan wanted to be a newspaper photographer, too.

As they began to wash the dishes, Susan asked, "Mama, please, may I have Dad's magic camera?"

"Maybe, when you're older."

"I'm big enough. I'll take good care of it," Susan said.

138

"Okay," her mother said, smiling as she gave

Susan the camera, "you will have to work very hard before that camera will be magic for you. I think your father was born to be a photographer, and even he had to practice, but you may try."

Susan did try very hard. Her mother showed her how to put film in the camera, but she didn't know photography and couldn't help much. Susan practiced every day, but when most of her pictures came back from the photography shop, they were not good at all. So she tried harder.

She knew that **The Star**, where her father had worked, wanted pictures that told a story. She thought, "If I take some pictures that tell a good story, maybe they will print them in **The Star**."

One day, Susan was outside with her camera when she heard sirens and saw smoke just down the street. She ran toward the fire.

A tall house was on fire, and firefighters were trying to put out the flames. Susan looked around and saw that no one from **The Star** was there.

Susan pointed the camera at a third story window where there was a lot of smoke. Just as she pushed the button, a young woman with a tiny baby in her arms climbed out over the windowsill. Susan and the others below took a deep breath.

There was no time for a ladder, so the firefighters quickly got a big, round net, then called to the woman to jump into it. The flames were almost to her now.

Susan was so afraid for the young woman and baby that she couldn't think. But something made her point the camera again, and, as the woman jumped, Susan pushed the button.

When she saw the woman and baby safe in the net, Susan took another picture. She took pictures of women from the crowd hugging the young woman and her baby, and of the young woman thanking the firefighters.

Then, a man ran up and said, "I'm from **The Star**. Did you take pictures of the woman who jumped?" Susan nodded. "If they're good, **The Star** will buy them. Come with me," he said.

At the newspaper, they asked Susan a lot of questions and took a picture of her. By that time, another man ran up and said Susan's pictures were very good.

That night, Susan and her mother couldn't wait to see the paper because all of Susan's pictures were on the front page. There was a story about her and her father in the paper, too.

"See, mother," Susan said, "Dad's camera worked like magic for me, too."

Her mother smiled and said, "Yes, Susan, but it's not the camera that's magic. It never was."

Margaret Bourke-White

We work with words.

wallet   wad
forgotten   gentleman
obey   favorite   Cuba

Sound the words.

wandered
army
miners
photographers

Margaret Bourke-White was one of the most famous photographers in the world. When she was young, she went to school to study animals, but later she became a photographer.

She became famous for telling story after story with her camera. In a way, she made it talk for her.

With her camera, she wandered over the world. She told about war with pictures she took for the army during World War II. She told about the hard life of African gold miners who worked deep in the earth, but she also told about famous people, both old and young.

Margaret Bourke-White took 250,000 photographs during her life, which is more than twenty pictures every day for almost thirty years.

The Human Family

We work with words.

motion   action   convention

Sound the word.

invention

Sight words.

What language would you hear
in Guatemala, Tunisia, or Israel?

Tunisia

Switzerland

Ivory Coast

Mexico

148

Every time a child is born, any place in the world, it will become a part of the human family. None of the people in this family look the same, or speak the same language. But no matter where in the world you go, you might say, "I'm not out of place here." This is because the invention of the camera has brought us pictures of our family from near and far.

Guatemala

Italy

Israel

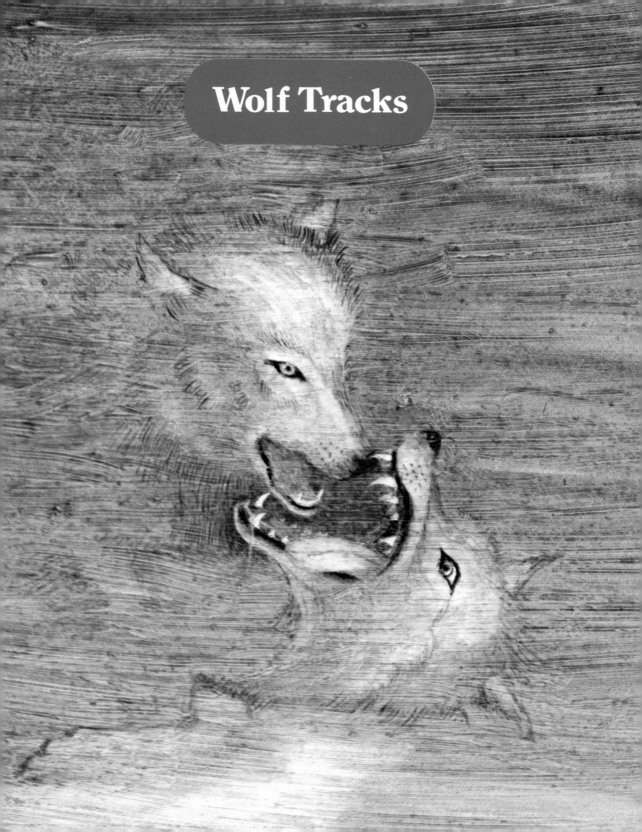

Wolf Tracks

In Search of the Real Wolf

We work with words.

disappear   discover

barge   ginger   margin

Sound the words.

display

largest

dug

favorite

wolf

Sight word.

The wolf is not a <u>villain</u>.

You can think of at least one favorite story for children in which a wolf takes the part of the villain. But who is the wolf, really?

The wolf is a member of the dog family and is most like the Eskimo sled dog. The wolf is the largest of all dogs. The largest wolf on record was over 79 kilograms (about 174 pounds), but most wolves are about 40 kilograms (about 88 pounds) when they are grown.

153

Wolves come in different colors, from black to white, but most of them are gray. The wolves in the far north can be white like the snow around them, and their hair is very thick to keep them warm during the long, cold winter.

Wolves have very big feet that keep them on top of the snow in winter and the mud in summer. Wolves often have to run over a large area to look for food. These big feet can carry them at a speed of up to 40 kilometers (about 25 miles) an hour if they are in a real hurry, but after an hour or two they will be dead tired. At a speed of eight kilometers (about 5 miles) an hour, they can run all night long and display no sign of slowing down.

Every wolf knows its place in its pack. When two wolves meet, one will hold its tail up, and the other will hold its down. This means there is agreement between the two about who will obey whom. If you look for these signs, you would see who is who in a wolf pack. This way there is peace between wolves without one feeling that it must display how strong and important it is every time it runs into another wolf.

A wolf has a wide head, pointed ears, a long, sharp nose, and eyes that look green in the dark. The long, sharp teeth of the wolf have made people think it is a bad animal.

Like all other animals in the dog family, wolves need to eat meat. You may give your dog meat from a can, but if it had no one to give it food, it would hunt for meat as the wolf does.

Here is where the wolf gets into trouble with people. The wolf likes to eat the same animals that a farmer wants to grow for people to eat. And so, for thousands of years and in all parts of the world, people have killed wolves to protect their animals — their meat.

The Wolf and the Caribou

The Eskimo people have a different way of looking at this trouble between people and wolves. This story was told to Farley Mowat, a man who made a study of wolves, by an Eskimo man named Ootek.

At the start of the world, there was a woman and a man, and nothing else walked, or swam, or flew in the world. Then one day, the woman dug a great hole in the ground and began to fish in it. One by one, she pulled out all the animals, and the last one she pulled out of the hole was the caribou. Then the god of the sky told the woman the caribou was the greatest present of all, for the caribou would be food for all the

people.

The woman let the caribou run free over the land, and soon the land was filled with caribou. The children of the woman knew how to hunt well, and found food and clothes and tents to live in, all from the caribou.

The children of the woman would hunt only the big, fat caribou. They had no wish to kill the weak and the small and the sick, since these were no good to eat.

After a time, there were more sick and weak caribou than fat and strong caribou, and the children saw this and talked to the woman about it.

Then the woman talked to the god of the sky and said, "Your work is no good, for the caribou are weak and sick, and if we eat them, we will grow weak and sick also."

He heard, and he said, "My work is good. I will tell the wolves, and they will eat the sick, and the weak, and the small caribou, so that the land will be left for the fat and the good ones."

And this is what happened, and this is why the wolf and the caribou are one. For the wolf may eat the caribou, but it is also the wolf who keeps the caribou strong.

Captain Salt's Problem

We work with words.

weary   wear   search
gentle   ginger   margin

Sound the words.

appeared
gentleman
passenger

At one time, an old sailor named Captain Salt lived in a house on a tiny island with a goat, a sheep, and a wolf. The sheep and goat grazed the tiny meadow and gave him wool and milk. The wolf was good company for the captain, keeping his feet warm at night. The three animals appeared to get along well. And as the captain said, "The wolf has been a perfect gentleman up to now." But all the same, Captain Salt knew that most wolves like sheep or goat meat, so he kept an eye out for trouble.

One dark night, there was a terrible storm. It seemed as if all the worst storms in the world had come together to make this one. It got so bad, the captain knew the only safe thing to do was row to the old lighthouse at the other side of his island.

His little boat could hold only one passenger besides the Captain, so he would have to make three trips.

Now here was his problem. He didn't want to leave the wolf alone with the sheep or the goat for fear the wolf would hurt them. How could he take all three animals, one at a time, to the lighthouse without leaving the wolf alone with one of the others?

The answer is below.

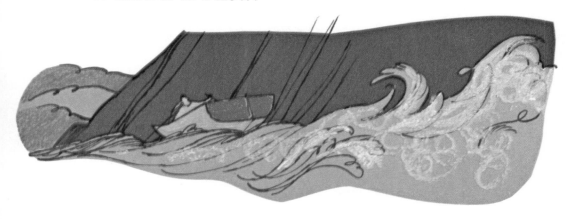

He first took the wolf to the lighthouse and returned for the sheep. When he left the sheep at the lighthouse, he picked up the wolf again and brought it back to his house. There he picked up the goat and left the wolf. After he brought the goat to the lighthouse, he went back for the wolf, and all four of them spent a warm and safe night at the lighthouse.

Goldie, the Wolf Pup

We work with words.

toss	host	loss
	mold	bold
gentle	gentleman	gym

Sound the words.

frost
Goldie
gently
den
forest
although

Goldie was a young wolf pup. Many things that mean a lot to human children were also important to Goldie — things like food, a good place to live, and others to be with. Like all wolves, Goldie needed to be part of a group.

Goldie woke one morning with her little, black nose deep in the hair of one of her sisters. She, two sisters, two brothers, and their mother slept close together in a den.

Their mother had dug the den into the side of a hill three weeks before they were born. She had dug a long hole with a little room in back. The world of the pups was small and dark at first, but now they were six weeks old and could go outside. So Goldie, her brothers and sisters, and their mother all went outside the den to join the rest of their family. Their wolf family was called a pack. There were several wolf packs in that forest. Each pack wandered and hunted in their own area and never went into the area of other wolves.

Although there was still frost on the ground the spring air felt good. Goldie ran down the hill from the den. Once she fell, but she got right up and ran again.

Suddenly, she was lifted off her feet and into the air. A big gray wolf had grabbed her at the back of her neck. Now she hung in his long teeth, and the frosted ground seemed far away. This wolf was Champ, her father. Strong enough to bring down a running deer, he gently carried Goldie back to the den. The leader of the pack, he had been watching the pups so they would not run away or get into trouble.

Wolves care for all wolf pups, not just their own, and they never leave the pups alone. When the mother and father had to be gone, one of the other grown wolves would babysit the pups.

All day long Goldie played with her brothers and sisters. When they were hungry, their mother nursed them. Once she heard a strange noise and chased them into the den. When she thought the danger was past, she let them back out to play.

As night came to the forest, the mother took the little pups back into the den while the bigger wolves lay down outside.

Goldie put her little black nose into her little tail and closed her eyes. Tomorrow would be another day — a busy day — in the life of a wolf pup.

The Outside Sense

We work with words.

strike strength

squirt squeal squirm

Sound the words.

stretched

squirrel

stronger

touched

The Wolf

The snap of fall was in the air. As the old wolf stood still, his head down, he suddenly heard the sound of the dogs — but they were still well behind him.

The wolf eyed the wire fence that stretched out before him, ugly and cold to the touch. And it could hurt too. He remembered back to when he was a pup when there were not many fences.

Because the dogs were closer, it was time to leave the meadow for the safety of the trees. The wolf, old as he was, jumped the fence with room to spare. As he ran toward the trees, he looked back at the dogs that looked so much like him. Soon the dogs saw him again and began to bark. They were building up their courage to try the fence, so the old wolf went quickly on his way.

A strange light came down through the trees. The wolf stopped to sniff the air. Winter was not far off. Soon the bright leaves would fall to the ground and there would be a thick blanket of red and yellow.

The wolf felt tired, so he rested. How strange it was to grow gray among these ever changing colors. Through half shut eyes, the wolf saw something move. It was quiet and small. A squirrel, he thought, or perhaps a rabbit. But he was not hungry. He wished only to sleep for a time in the warm sun.

But before he shut his eyes, the smell of an old enemy reached him. It was a human smell. He was sure of it. The wolf was quickly up and moving.

The smell became stronger, but there was no sound. A sense outside the wolf told him to go on, but then, at the foot of a giant tree, he saw it — a young human.

For several minutes the old wolf stood and watched. When the thing on the ground did not move, the wolf grew braver, put aside his fear and slowly walked forward.

At last, when the young human made a sound, the wolf came to a stop. Why was the human this deep in the woods when it was almost dark? But now the wolf was close enough to see the reason — beside the human was a large branch. As the wolf looked up to see where it had broken from the tree, the human made another soft sound. It made the wolf think of the way cubs sound in the den. Slowly, the wolf came closer. The wolf sniffed again and then touched the human with his nose. The young human was very cold.

The old wolf looked up at the sky. It was almost dark. Quiet filled the woods. The only sounds were the night howls of the birds and the wind in the trees. The outside sense told the wolf to lie down beside the human.

It grew colder, and the wolf moved closer.
Every so often, the human would make that
same, soft sound. Once, the human even reached
out and touched him.

Marta

We work with words.   Sound the words.

racing   living   crumpled   continued

bank   monk   bunk   blink

decision   vision   version

Marta

As the girl continued to dream, she felt herself falling, falling, falling. Since she moved little in her sleep, it was not until the middle of the night that she noticed she was not alone. It's Lobo, she thought, and her hand again reached out and touched the warm body beside her.

The wolf felt the human move, but stayed where he was because the hand that had touched him had not hurt.

Several minutes passed, and then the wolf heard something moving in the dry leaves. Like a great gray ghost, he rose and stood beside the sleeping girl. In the dark, he could see a pair of yellow eyes. A low growl came from the wolf's throat.

The yellow eyes began to move. They were coming closer. He left the girl and moved toward the eyes. The wolf was a large animal, well over 110 pounds. There was nothing in these woods that was his equal. The wolf saw the eyes blink once, twice, and then move away. He returned to his place by the girl.

The clouds began to race across the sky.

For a little while, the wolf could see the moon,
but the clouds moved quickly over it. It was not
until the first light of the sun that he felt he must
leave.

Now everything inside the wolf said, "Run,
run to a deeper part of the woods!" But a sense
outside him held him fast when the wolf felt the
girl's hand once again touch him.

But then it was decided — he rose slowly,
turned, and ran back toward the fence.

"No, Lobo!" the man yelled. But the dog
was beyond his control. On the other side of the
fence was another version of himself, a great
gray ghost from his past.

"No, Lobo. He's too big for you, boy!" shouted the man. "Come back!" But at that second, the dog jumped over the fence.

As quickly as he could, the man was through the fence and running after his dog. He followed the sound of the barking, as the dog chased the gray shape through the woods.

The man ran on and on, listening only to his dog.

Then suddenly, the running stopped. In front of him were his daughter and the dog. A great gray shape grew small as it ran deeper into the woods.

"Marta, thank goodness you're safe," said the father.

"I fell out of the tree," said the girl. Her hand reached for the dog beside her. "It was a good thing that Lobo found me last night."

The man's eyes went from the dog to the place where he had seen the gray shape run into the woods.

A strange look came into the father's eyes. "Marta," he said. "Lobo has never left my side. We've been looking for you all night."

Glossary

Key to Pronunciation

Listed below are diacritical symbols and key words. The boldface letters in the key words represent the sounds indicated by the symbols.

/ā/	c**a**ke	/ō/	r**o**pe
/a/	h**a**t	/o/	t**o**p
/ä/	f**a**ther	/ô/	s**a**w
/är/	c**ar**	/oi/	**oi**l
/âr/	c**are**	/o͞o/	m**oo**n
/b/	**b**oy	/o͝o/	b**oo**k
/ch/	**ch**ur**ch**	/ôr/	f**or**k
/d/	**d**uck	/ou/	**ou**t
/ē/	b**ea**n	/p/	**p**et
/e/	p**e**t	/r/	**r**un
/f/	**f**un	/s/	**s**ee
/g/	**g**o	/sh/	**sh**ip
/gz/	e**x**act	/t/	**t**op
/h/	**h**ome	/th/	**th**in
/(h)w/	**wh**ite	/t͟h/	**th**is
/ī/	p**ie**	/u/	n**u**t
/i/	p**i**g	/ûr/	f**ur**
/ir/	d**ear**	/v/	**v**ine
/j/	**j**ump	/w/	**w**ill
/k/	**k**ite	/y/	**y**es
/ks/	bo**x**	/y͞oo/	**u**se
/kw/	**qu**it	/z/	**z**oo
/l/	**l**ook	/zh/	a**z**ure
/m/	**m**an	/ə/	**a**bove
/n/	**n**ot		**ci**rcu**s**
/ng/	si**ng**	/ər/	butt**er**

Aa

ac·ci·dents [ak′sə·dənts]. Unlucky events that cause damage or harm, such as collisions, falls, etc.

a·dults [ə·dults′ or ad′ults]. Persons who have come of age, usually 21 or older.

a·gree·ment [ə·grē′mənt]. A sameness or harmony of opinion.

air·craft [âr′kraft′]. Any machine or vehicle designed to travel from place to place through the air, as airplanes, balloons, and helicopters.

al·lit·er·a·tion [ə·lit′ə·rā′shən]. The use of the same sound at the beginnings of stressed words in a group or line of verse, as the f's in the phrase "A fair field full of folk."

an·kle [ang′kəl]. The joint connecting the foot and the leg.

an·tique [an·tēk′]. Something made long ago, as furniture, china, silver, etc.

At·lan·tis [at·lan′tis]. In Greek myths, an island that was engulfed by the sea.

a·vi·a·tion [ā′vē·ā′shən]. The science or techniques of building and flying aircraft.

Bb

barn·storm·er [bärn′stôrm′ər]. One who tours rural districts giving shows, making speeches, or giving exhibitions of stunt flying.

beat [bēt]. 1. The basic unit of musical time. 2. Rhythm.

beau·ty [byōō′tē]. The quality in a person or thing that delights the eye, the ear, or the mind.

be·yond [bi·yond′]. Outside the reach or scope of: *beyond* help.

blink [blingk]. To wink rapidly.

blues [blōōs]. A song, or songs, of a type originated by the American Negro, having a mournful melody and sad words.

bod·ies [bod′ēs]. The entire physical parts of persons, animals, or plants.

bound [bound]. On the way; headed; going: *bound* for home.

brass [bras]. The brass instruments of an orchestra, taken together.

brush [brush]. A growth of small trees and shrubs.

bu·gle [byōō′gəl]. A kind of small trumpet, usually not having keys or valves. It is used to sound out orders and signals, as to soldiers.

bush [bŏŏsh]. A low, treelike shrub with many branches or stems.

Cc

car·i·bou [kar′ə·bōō]. Any of several kinds of reindeer found in North America.

cause [kôz]. To make happen; bring about: Fear *caused* his voice to tremble.

cel·e·brate [sel′ə·brāt]. To observe or honor in a special manner: to *celebrate* a holiday.

cen·ti·me·ters [sen′tə·mē′tərs]. Measurements of length each equal to 1/100 of a meter. One inch is about 2.54 centimeters.

clar·i·net [klar′ə·net′]. A high-pitched woodwind musical instrument having a cylindrical body and a single-reed mouthpiece.

climbed [klīmd]. To have gone up or down by means of the feet and sometimes the hands: to have *climbed* a mountain.

com·put·er [kəm·pyōō′tər]. An electronic device capable of doing arithmetic with great speed and accuracy, widely used in industry and business for handling masses of information automatically and for timing and controlling other devices.

con·tin·ued [kən·tin′yōōd]. To have gone on or persisted in an action or condition: They *continued* to try.

con·trol [kən·trol′]. A controlled or guided condition; restraint: Everything is under *control*; a car out of *control*.

cor·net [kôr·net]. A brass musical instrument like a trumpet.

cou·ple [kup′əl]. A man and woman who are married, engaged, partners in a dance, etc.

courts [kôrts]. Places where law cases are tried.

crops [krops]. Farm products, growing or harvested, as cotton, corn, hay, or apples.

crowd·ed [kroud′ed]. Condition caused by a large number of people being gathered closely together.

cubs [kubz]. The young of certain animals, such as the bear, fox, wolf, or lion.

cu·ri·ous [kyo͞or′ē·əs]. Eager to know or learn more.

Dd

da·guerre·o·types [dəger′ə·tīps′]. Old-fashioned photographs made on silver-coated metal plates sensitive to light.

daugh·ter [dô′tər]. A girl or woman, considered in relation to either or both of her parents.

de·mand·ed [di·mand′ed]. 1. To have asked for boldly; to have claimed as a right: The man *demanded* a lawyer. 2. To ask for forcefully: The teacher *demanded* an answer.

den [den]. The cave or resting place of a wild animal; lair.

dis·play [dis·plā′]. 1. To show in a way that attracts notice; exhibit: to *display* goods. 2. To show openly; reveal: to *display* skill.

Ee

earth·quake [ûrth′kwāk′]. A shaking or vibration of a part of the earth's surface, caused by an underground shift, volcanic action, etc.

eld·er·ly [el′dər·lē]. Approaching old age; rather old.

el·e·va·tors [el′ə·vā′tərs]. Movable, usually enclosed platforms or cages for carrying passenger or freight up and down, as inside a building.

else [els]. Other; different or more: I want something *else*.

e·nough [i·nuf′]. Sufficient for what is needed or wanted: There is *enough* cake for everyone.

e·qual [ē′kwəl]. A person or thing having the same elements, size, or other features as another: She is his *equal* in ability.

e·vents [i·vents′]. Happenings; occurrences, especially important ones: historical *events*.

ex·act·ly [ig·zakt′lē]. In an exact manner; precisely.

eyed [īd]. To have looked at or watched carefully: They *eyed* each other with distrust.

Ff

fad·ed [fād′ed]. Has grown dimmer and slowly disappeared.

fa·mous [fā′məs]. Very well known and often mentioned or praised.

fa·vor·ite [fā′vər·it]. Best loved: my *favorite* song.

fig·ure [fig′yər]. A visible outline or form; shape; a human form: to glimpse a ghostly *figure*.

film [film]. A sheet, roll, or strip of material having a thin coating of a chemical substance that is sensitive to light, used for making photographs.

fire·fight·ers [fīr′fī′tərs]. Persons who put out fires.

flames [flāmz]. 1. The burning gas rising from a fire, usually in glowing orange or yellow tongues. 2. A burning condition: in *flames*.

fu·el [fyo͞o′əl]. Something that readily produces energy in the form of heat when burnt as wood, coal, oil, etc.

furs [fûrz]. 1. The soft, hairy coats of many animals, as foxes, seals, squirrels, etc. 2. Cleaned animal skins covered with such coats.

Gg

gears [girs]. Mechanisms to do something.

gen·tle·man [jen′təl·mən]. A courteous, refined, and honorable man.

glid·er [glī′dər]. A light aircraft like an airplane but without an engine. It is kept aloft by air currents.

good·ness [go͝od′nis]. A word to express surprise or emphasis: *Goodness*, but you're late!

grazed [grāzd]. To have been fed on growing grass: Cattle *grazed* whenever hungry.

grind [grīnd]. 1. To press together with a scraping motion; grate: to *grind* the teeth. 2. To produce mechanically, or with effort.

grown [grōn]. Fully developed; mature; adult: a *grown* man.

guests [gests]. Persons received or entertained by another or others, especially at a meal or party, or for a visit.

Hh

haunt·ed [hôn′tid]. Often visited by ghosts or spirits: The story took place in a *haunted* castle.

health [helth]. General condition of the body and mind: good *health*, poor *health*.

high [hī]. Raised in pitch; shrill: a *high* sound.

hos·es [hōz·ez]. Easily bending tubes, often of rubber, through which water, etc., may be forced.

hours [ourz]. The 24 equal periods making up a day; there are 60 minutes in each *hour*.

hu·mans [(h)yo͞o′məns]. Men, women, or children; persons. The more formal term is human beings.

hut [hut]. A small, crude house or cabin.

hy·per·bo·le [hī·pûr′bə·lē]. An obviously exaggerated statement made for dramatic effect, as in "He's as tough as nails."

Ii

ice·bergs [īs′bûrgz′]. Thick masses of ice separated from a glacier and floating in the ocean.

id·i·om [id'ē·əm]. 1. An expression having a special meaning different from the usual meaning of the words. "To put up with" is an idiom meaning "to tolerate or endure." 2. The language or dialect of a region, profession, or social class: Scottish *idiom;* legal *idiom*.

index [in'deks]. A list in alphabetical order of topics, names, etc., at the end of a book, showing on which page or pages each appears.

In·di·an [in'dē·ən]. 1. A member of any of the races of people inhabiting North and South America when European explorers came to the New World. 2. A native of India.

in·stru·ments [in'strə·mənts]. Devices or systems for measuring, recording, or controlling, as those found in a car or airplane.

in·ven·tion [in·ven'shən]. Something invented.

is·land [ī'lənd]. A body of land entirely surrounded by water.

Jj

jam [jam]. A number of people or things crowded together: a traffic *jam*.

jazz [jaz]. 1. A kind of popular music that originated with Negroes in the southern U.S. 2. A jazz band: *jazz* musicians.

junk [jungk]. Worthless or worn-out things; trash; rubbish.

Kk

kil·o·grams [kil'ə·grams']. In the metric system, units often used to measure weight, each equal to 1,000 grams, or about 2.2 pounds.

knobs [nobs]. Rounded handles, as on doors, radios, etc.

Ll

lan·guage [lang'gwij]. The words which a certain nation or group uses in speaking and writing: the French *language*.

leath·er [leth'ər]. Animal skin or hide, usually with the hair or fur removed, and made ready for many uses by cleaning and tanning.

light·house [līt'hous']. A tower equipped with a powerful light and used to guide ships or warn them of rocks and similar dangers.

lyr·ics [lir'iks]. The words of a popular song.

Mm

man·u·al [man'yōō·əl]. A small guidebook, reference book, or book of instructions; handbook.

mar·ble [mär'bəl]. A hard, partly crystallized limestone occurring in many colors, used for building, sculpture, etc.: a *marble* statue.

mead·ow [med'ō]. A tract of land where grass is grown for hay or for grazing.

mel·o·dy [mel'ə·dē]. A meaningful succession of musical tones in a single part or voice; tune.

179

mem·ber [mem′bər]. 1. A person or creature who belongs to a group, as a family, club, legislature, etc. 2. An element of a set or of any whole thing.

min·ers [mīn′ərs]. Persons who work digging minerals from the earth.

mis·take [mis·tāk′]. 1. An error or blunder. 2. To take to be another: to *mistake* a friend for an enemy.

mu·si·cians [myo͞o·zish′əns]. Persons who are skilled in music, especially professional composers or performers of music.

myth [mith]. 1. A traditional story, usually about gods, heroes, etc., often offering an explanation of something in nature or of past events. 2. Any made-up story, person, event, etc.

Nn

neg·a·tive [neg′ə·tiv]. In photography, having the light and dark areas reversed.

non·stop [non′stop′]. Without making a stop: a *nonstop* train; to fly *nonstop*.

Oo

o·bey [ō·bā′]. To do the bidding of; submit to: to *obey* one's superiors.

of·fi·cer [of′ə·sər]. A policeman.

on·ion [un′yən]. The juicy bulb of a plant of the lily family, having a strong odor and taste. Onions are eaten raw or used in cooking.

owned [ōnd]. To have had as one's property: to have possessed.

Pp

pack [pak]. A group of wolves or dogs that hunt together.

pas·sen·ger [pas′ən·jər]. A person riding in but not driving, a bus, train, plane, etc.

phan·tom [fan′təm]. 1. Something that exists only in the imagination but seems to be real. 2. A ghost. 3. Ghostlike: a *phantom* ship.

pho·tog·ra·pher [fə·tog′rə·fər]. A person who takes pictures or makes a business of photography.

pho·tog·ra·phy [fə·tog′rə·fē]. 1. The process or art of forming and preserving an image by using the chemical action of light on a sensitive film in a camera. 2. The art or business of producing and printing photographs.

post [pōst]. A store: trading *post*.

pow·der [pou′dər]. 1. A dry mass of fine particles made by crushing or grinding a solid substance. 2. Any kind of powder prepared in this way.

pro·tect [prə·tekt′]. To shield or defend from attack, harm, or injury; guard; shelter.

pup [pup]. 1. A young dog; puppy. 2. A young seal or shark or any of the young of certain other animals.

Qq

qui·et·ly [kwī′ət·lē]. Making little or no noise: The machine runs *quietly*.

Rr

rag·time [rag′tīm]. An early form of jazz using fast, syncopated rhythms.

rest·less [rest′lis]. Unable to rest or be still; nervous; uneasy.

rhythm [rith′əm]. 1. The repetition of a beat, sound, accent, motion, etc. 2. A particular arrangement of lengths and stresses in music or poetry: march *rhythm*.

roar [rôr]. A loud noise: the *roar* of a cannon; the *roar* of an engine.

row [rō]. To propel (a boat) by using oars.

ru·in [rōō′in]. 1. The remains of something that has decayed or been destroyed: the *ruins* of bombed cities. 2. To destroy, demolish, or damage.

Ss

scale [skāl]. 1. A series of lines and marks placed at regular intervals on an instrument for measuring various quantities, amounts, etc.: the *scale* on a yardstick. 2. Any system of such graduated lines or marks adapted for a special purpose: the Fahrenheit *scale;* a logarithmic *scale*.

sharp [shärp]. Coming to or having a point: a *sharp* peak.

shoul·der [shōl′dər]. The part of the body to which the arm in man, an animal's foreleg, or a bird's wing is jointed.

sig·nal [sig′nəl]. To inform by using a sign or signs: The driver ahead *signaled* me to pass him.

sim·i·le [sim′ə·lē]. A figure of speech in which one thing is compared to another that is different in many ways, by the use of *as* or *like*. "He is as stupid as an ox" is a simile.

sin·gle [sing′gəl]. One alone; separate; individual: Not a *single* star is visible.

si·rens [sī′rəns]. Devices that give out a loud, piercing wail or whistle, used as warning signals: the *sirens* on police cars.

slav·er·y [slā′vər·ē]. 1. The practice of holding human beings as slaves. 2. The condition of being a slave: freed from *slavery*.

sled [sled]. A vehicle on runners, used for carrying people or loads over snow and ice.

sneered [snird]. To have shown dislike or contempt in speech, writing, etc.

song·fest [sông′fest]. Singing of popular or folk songs by an informal group; a singing festival.

spare [spâr]. Extra or available: *spare* parts.

spar·klers [spär′klərs]. Thin, rodlike fireworks that give off sparks when lighted.

spir·it [spir′it]. 1. Any of various supernatural beings, as ghosts, goblins, elves, etc. 2. Loyalty or devotion: school *spirit*.

spite [spīt]. Despite: notwithstanding: In *spite* of all his troubles, he was always cheerful.

stared [stârd]. looked at fixedly.

181

stub·born [stub′ərn]. Hard to persuade or convince; not giving in easily; obstinate.

swamp [swomp]. An area of low, wet land; bog; marsh.

switch [swich]. A device for making or breaking a connection in an electrical circuit.

Tt

tam·bou·rine [tam′bə·rēn′]. A shallow drum with jingling metal disks in the sides, played by shaking or striking with the hand.

tem·po [tem′pō]. The relative speed at which a piece of music is played.

the·a·ter [thē′ə·tər]. A place built for the presentation of plays, films, etc.

through [thro͞o]. From one place to another or to all parts of: to ride *through* the streets.

tribes [trībz]. Groups of people, often primitive people, each having a leader and usually sharing the same customs, religious beliefs, etc.

trom·bone [trom·bōn′ *or* trom′bōn′]. A brass instrument related to the trumpet, but larger and lower in pitch than the trumpet.

trum·pet [trum′pit]. A brass instrument of high range with a flaring bell and a long, curved metal tube, whose pitch is varied by means of valves.

twins [twinz]. Two persons or things that are very much alike.

Uu

up·set [up·set′]. To disturb mentally: The bad news *upset* us all.

Vv

va·ca·tion [vā·kā′shən]. A period of time for rest or recreation, away from regular work, study, etc.

ver·sion [vûr′zhən]. A particular form or adaption of something: a movie *version* of a play.

vil·lain [vil′ən]. A wicked or evil person, especially a wicked character in a novel, play, etc.

voic·es [vois′·es]. 1. The sounds made through the mouth of persons, or animals, especially the sounds made by human beings in speaking, singing, etc. 2. The quality or character of one's vocal sound: a melodious *voice*.

Ww

waif's [wāfs]. Belonging to, or for a homeless, lost, or abandoned creature, especially a child or a pet.

wan·dered [won′dərd]. To have taken an irregular, twisting route: The stream *wandered* by.

weak [wēk]. Lacking in strength or effectiveness: to be *weak* after a long illness.

ACKNOWLEDGMENTS

For permission to adapt and reprint copyrighted materials, grateful acknowledgment is made to the following publishers, authors, and other copyright holders:

American Heritage Publishing Company, Inc., for "Crashing Coast to Coast" by Sherwood Harris. Adapted from an article in the October 1964 issue of *American Heritage* Magazine. Reprinted by permission. Copyright © 1964 American Heritage Publishing Co., Inc.

Boys' Life, for "The Richter Scale." Adapted and reprinted permission of *Boys' Life,* published by the Boy Scouts of America.

Carol Carrick, author, for "Captain Salt's Problem," from "Cap'n Salt Outwits the Wolf" by Carol Carrick, copyright © 1976 by Carol Carrick. Adapted and reprinted by permission of the author.

Houghton Mifflin Company, for "The House That Wasn't There" by Louis C. Jones. Adapted from *Spooks of the Valley* by Louis C. Jones. Copyright 1948 by Louis C. Jones. Copyright © 1975 by Louis C. Jones. Reprinted by permission of Houghton Mifflin Company.

The John Day Company and Harold Ober Associates Incorporated, for "The Big Wave" by Pearl S. Buck. Adapted from *The Big Wave* by Pearl S. Buck. Copyright, 1947, by the Curtis Publishing Company. Copyright, 1948, by Pearl S. Buck. Copyright renewed. Used with permission of The John Day Company and reprinted by permission of Harold Ober Associates Incorporated.

J. B. Lippincott Company, for "The Strange Ride" by Seymour Simon, adapted from *Ghosts* by Seymour Simon, copyright © 1976 by Seymour Simon, reprinted by permission of J. B. Lippincott Company, and J. B. Lippincott Company and Curtis Brown, Ltd., for "His Robot Buddy" by Alfred Slote, adapted from *My Robot Buddy* by Alfred Slote, copyright © 1975 by Alfred Slote, reprinted by permission of J. B. Lippincott Company and Curtis Brown, Ltd.

Little, Brown and Company, McClelland and Stewart Limited, and Hughes Massie, Ltd., for "The Wolf and the Caribou" adapted from *Never Cry Wolf* by Farley Mowat. Copyright © 1963 by Farley Mowat. Reprinted by permission of Little, Brown and Co.; The Canadian Publishers, McClelland and Stewart Limited, Toronto; and Hughes Massie, Ltd.

McGraw-Hill Book Company, for "Who Cares" by Virginia Brown, Billie Phillips, and Elsa Joffe. From *Who Cares* by Virginia Brown et al. Copyright © 1965 by McGraw-Hill, Inc. Used with permission of McGraw-Hill Book Company.

Julian Messner, for "City of Mud" and "Strange but True" adapted from *Chicago: Crossroads of American Enterprise* by Dorsha B. Hayes. Copyright © 1944, 1971 by Dorsha B. Hayes. Reprinted by permission of Julian Messner, a Simon & Schuster division of Gulf & Western Corporation.

Plenary Publications International, Inc., for reproductions on page 56. Reproduced from Volume 1 of *The Family Creative Workshop* series, distributed by Time-Life Books. Copyright © 1974 Product Development International Holding, n.v. All rights reserved. No part of this work may be used or reproduced in any manner without the written permission of the copyright holder.

Science Digest, for "The Robot Firefighter" from the article "Robot to the Rescue." Reprinted by permission of *Science Digest.* Copyright © 1972 The Hearst Corporation.

Charles Scribner's Sons, for "New York to Paris" by Alice Dalgliesh. Adapted from *Ride on the Wind* by Alice Dalgliesh with the permission of Charles Scribner's Sons. Copyright © 1956 Charles Scribner's Sons.

The Viking Press, Inc., for "The White House Ghosts" by Maria Leach. Adapted from *Whistle in the Graveyard* by Maria Leach. Copyright © 1974 by Maria Leach. By permission of The Viking Press.

Grateful acknowledgment is made to the following for reproduction of photographs and color transparencies on the pages indicated:

Erik Arnesen, Don Murie Productions 148, 150; Margaret Bourke-White, *Life* Magazine, © Time Inc. 143-146; The Chicago Association of Commerce and Industry 67; *Chicago Tribune* Photos 81, 83; *Ebony* Magazine, Johnson Publishing Company 83; Yoram Kahana, Don Murie Productions 147, 149, 150; The Museum of Modern Art/Film Stills Archive 41; National Aeronautics and Space Administration 43; National Air and Space Museum, Smithsonian Institution 43, 44, 48, 50; National Oceanic and Atmospheric Administration 19, 20; NCT Ltd. 82; Underwood and Underwood News Photos 45, 53; Official United States Air Force Photograph 43; United States Department of the Interior Geological Survey 21; University of Illinois Library at Chicago Circle Campus, Jane Addams Memorial Collection 75, 77.

Grateful acknowledgment is made to the following for illustrations on the pages indicated:

The Bettmann Archive, Inc. 43, 54, 55, 88, 94; Ellen Blonder 136, 139, 140, 142; April Funcke 24, 79, 115, 116, 119, 120; Barbara Hack 89; Christa Kieffer-Mitchell 16-18, 95; Heather King 165, 167, 169, 170, 172-174; William Mathison 37; Lyle Miller 68-73; Tom Newsom 90-92; Norman Prince 25, 31, 34, 36, 132, 133, 135; Steve Reoutt 57, 58, 60, 61, 64, 66, 121-123, 125, 128, 130; Phil Smith 26, 29, 30, 104-109, 111, 112, 159, 161, 162; Karen Tucker 96, 97, 100-103; Connie Warton 8, 9, 11-15, 22, 151-153, 155-158; Gordon Willman 84, 85, 87.